To Celebrate

_____

_____

Date

_____

THANK YOU FOR COMING.

Let's celebrate!

ISBN: 978-83-958237-6-3

Guest Name

_____

Wishes & Messages

_____

_____

_____

_____

_____

_____

Email/Phone

Guest Name

Wishes & Messages

EMAIL/PHONE

Guest Name

_____

Wishes & Messages

_____

_____

_____

_____

_____

_____

EMAIL/PHONE _____

Guest Name

Wishes & Messages

Email/Phone

Guest Name

_____

Wishes & Messages

_____

_____

_____

_____

_____

Email/Phone _____

Guest Name

_____

Wishes & Messages

_____

_____

_____

_____

_____

_____

Email/Phone _____

Guest Name

_____

Wishes & Messages

_____

_____

_____

_____

_____

EMAIL/PHONE
_____

Guest Name

_____

Wishes & Messages

_____

_____

_____

_____

_____

_____

Email/Phone

Guest Name

_____

Wishes & Messages

_____

_____

_____

_____

_____

Email/Phone
_____

Guest Name

_____

Wishes & Messages

_____

_____

_____

_____

_____

_____

Email/Phone

Guest Name

_____

Wishes & Messages

_____

_____

_____

_____

_____

_____

Email/Phone

Guest Name

Wishes & Messages

Email/Phone

Guest Name

_____

Wishes & Messages

_____

_____

_____

_____

_____

Email/Phone
_____

Guest Name

Wishes & Messages

Guest Name

_____

Wishes & Messages

_____

_____

_____

_____

_____

_____

Email/Phone

Guest Name

_____

Wishes & Messages

_____

_____

_____

_____

_____

_____
Email/Phone

Guest Name

_____

Wishes & Messages

_____

_____

_____

_____

_____

Email/Phone
_____

Guest Name

Wishes & Messages

Email/Phone

Guest Name

Wishes & Messages

Email/Phone

Guest Name

Wishes & Messages

_____

_____

_____

_____

_____

EMAIL/PHONE

Guest Name

_____

Wishes & Messages

_____

_____

_____

_____

_____

_____

EMAIL/PHONE
_____

Guest Name

_____

Wishes & Messages

_____

_____

_____

_____

_____

_____
Email/Phone

Guest Name
_____

Wishes & Messages

_____
_____
_____
_____
_____
_____

Email/Phone

Guest Name

Wishes & Messages

EMAIL/PHONE

Guest Name

_____

Wishes & Messages

_____

_____

_____

_____

_____

EMAIL/PHONE _____

Guest Name

Wishes & Messages

Email/Phone

Guest Name

_____

Wishes & Messages

_____

_____

_____

_____

_____

_____

Email/Phone

Guest Name

_____

Wishes & Messages

_____

_____

_____

_____

_____

_____

Email/Phone

Guest Name

_____

Wishes & Messages

_____

_____

_____

_____

_____

Email/Phone
_____

Guest Name

_____

Wishes & Messages

_____

_____

_____

_____

_____

EMAIL/PHONE

Guest Name

_____

Wishes & Messages

_____

_____

_____

_____

_____

_____

EMAIL/PHONE
_____

Guest Name

_____

Wishes & Messages

_____

_____

_____

_____

_____

Email/Phone
_____

Guest Name

Wishes & Messages

_____

_____

_____

_____

_____

_____

EMAIL/PHONE

Guest Name

Wishes & Messages

_____

_____

_____

_____

_____

_____

EMAIL/PHONE

Guest Name

_____

Wishes & Messages

_____

_____

_____

_____

_____

Email/Phone _____

Guest Name

_____

Wishes & Messages

_____

_____

_____

_____

_____

_____

Email/Phone

Guest Name

_____

Wishes & Messages

_____

_____

_____

_____

_____

EMAIL/PHONE _____

Guest Name

Wishes & Messages

Email/Phone

Guest Name

_____

Wishes & Messages

_____

_____

_____

_____

_____

_____

Email/Phone

Guest Name

Wishes & Messages

Email/Phone

Guest Name

_____

Wishes & Messages

_____

_____

_____

_____

_____

_____

Email/Phone
_____

Guest Name

_____

Wishes & Messages

_____

_____

_____

_____

_____

_____

Email/Phone

Guest Name

_____

Wishes & Messages

_____

_____

_____

_____

_____

_____

Email/Phone

Guest Name

Wishes & Messages

EMAIL/PHONE

Guest Name

_____

Wishes & Messages

_____

_____

_____

_____

_____

_____

Email/Phone
_____

Guest Name

_____

Wishes & Messages

_____

_____

_____

_____

_____

_____

EMAIL/PHONE

Guest Name

_____

Wishes & Messages

_____

_____

_____

_____

_____

_____
EMAIL/PHONE

Guest Name

_____

Wishes & Messages

_____

_____

_____

_____

_____

_____

Email/Phone
_____

Guest Name

Wishes & Messages

Email/Phone

Guest Name

_____

Wishes & Messages

_____

_____

_____

_____

_____

_____

Email/Phone _____

Guest Name

_____

Wishes & Messages

_____

_____

_____

_____

_____

_____

EMAIL/PHONE

Guest Name

Wishes & Messages

EMAIL/PHONE

Guest Name

Wishes & Messages

Email/Phone

Guest Name

Wishes & Messages

_____

_____

_____

_____

_____

_____

Email/Phone

Guest Name

_____

Wishes & Messages

_____

_____

_____

_____

_____

EMAIL/PHONE
_____

Guest Name

Wishes & Messages

_____

_____

_____

_____

_____

EMAIL/PHONE

Guest Name

Wishes & Messages

Email/Phone

Guest Name

_____

Wishes & Messages

_____

_____

_____

_____

_____

_____

Email/Phone

Guest Name

_____

Wishes & Messages

_____

_____

_____

_____

_____

_____

EMAIL/PHONE

Guest Name

Wishes & Messages

E
EMAIL/PHONE

Guest Name

_____

Wishes & Messages

_____

_____

_____

_____

_____

Email/Phone
_____

Guest Name

_____

Wishes & Messages

_____

_____

_____

_____

_____

Email/Phone _____

Guest Name

_____

Wishes & Messages

_____

_____

_____

_____

_____

EMAIL/PHONE _____

Guest Name

Wishes & Messages

_____

_____

_____

_____

_____

Email/Phone

Guest Name

_____

Wishes & Messages

_____

_____

_____

_____

_____

_____

EMAIL/PHONE
_____

Guest Name

Wishes & Messages

_____

_____

_____

_____

_____

_____

Email/Phone

Guest Name

_____

Wishes & Messages

_____

_____

_____

_____

_____

_____

Email/Phone
_____

Guest Name

_____

Wishes & Messages

_____

_____

_____

_____

_____

_____

Email/Phone _____

Guest Name

_____

Wishes & Messages

_____

_____

_____

_____

_____

_____

EMAIL/PHONE
_____

Guest Name

Wishes & Messages

Email/Phone

Guest Name

_____

Wishes & Messages

_____

_____

_____

_____

_____

_____

EMAIL/PHONE

Guest Name

_____

Wishes & Messages

_____

_____

_____

_____

_____

EMAIL/PHONE
_____

Guest Name

_____

Wishes & Messages

_____

_____

_____

_____

_____

_____

Email/Phone
_____

Guest Name

_____

Wishes & Messages

_____

_____

_____

_____

_____

_____

Email/Phone

Guest Name

_____

Wishes & Messages

_____

_____

_____

_____

_____

_____

EMAIL/PHONE

Guest Name

_____

Wishes & Messages

_____

_____

_____

_____

_____

_____

Email/Phone

Guest Name

_____

Wishes & Messages

_____

_____

_____

_____

_____

_____

EMAIL/PHONE

Guest Name

_____

Wishes & Messages

_____

_____

_____

_____

_____

_____

EMAIL/PHONE

Guest Name

_____

Wishes & Messages

_____

_____

_____

_____

_____

_____

EMAIL/PHONE

Guest Name

Wishes & Messages

EMAIL/PHONE

Guest Name

_____

Wishes & Messages

_____

_____

_____

_____

_____

Email/Phone
_____

Guest Name

_____

Wishes & Messages

_____

_____

_____

_____

_____

_____

Email/Phone

Guest Name

_____

Wishes & Messages

_____

_____

_____

_____

_____

_____

EMAIL/PHONE

Guest Name

_____

Wishes & Messages

_____

_____

_____

_____

_____

_____

EMAIL/PHONE

Guest Name

Wishes & Messages

Email/Phone

Guest Name

_____

Wishes & Messages

_____

_____

_____

_____

_____

Email/Phone

Guest Name

_____

Wishes & Messages

_____

_____

_____

_____

_____

_____

EMAIL/PHONE
_____

Guest Name

_____

Wishes & Messages

_____

_____

_____

_____

_____

EMAIL/PHONE
_____

Guest Name

Wishes & Messages

EMAIL/PHONE

Guest Name

_____

Wishes & Messages

_____

_____

_____

_____

_____

_____

Email/Phone

Guest Name

_____

Wishes & Messages

_____

_____

_____

_____

_____

_____

Email/Phone

Guest Name

_____

Wishes & Messages

_____

_____

_____

_____

_____

EMAIL/PHONE _____

Guest Name

_____

Wishes & Messages

_____

_____

_____

_____

_____

_____

Email/Phone _____

Guest Name

_____

Wishes & Messages

_____

_____

_____

_____

_____

EMAIL/PHONE
_____

Guest Name

_____

Wishes & Messages

_____

_____

_____

_____

_____

_____

Email/Phone

Guest Name

_____

Wishes & Messages

_____

_____

_____

_____

_____

_____

EMAIL/PHONE _____

Guest Name

_____

Wishes & Messages

_____

_____

_____

_____

_____

EMAIL/PHONE
_____

Guest Name

Wishes & Messages

_____

_____

_____

_____

_____

_____

Email/Phone

Guest Name

_____

Wishes & Messages

_____

_____

_____

_____

_____

_____

EMAIL/PHONE

Guest Name

_____

Wishes & Messages

_____

_____

_____

_____

_____

EMAIL/PHONE
_____

Guest Name

_____

Wishes & Messages

_____

_____

_____

_____

_____

_____

Email/Phone _____

Guest Name

Wishes & Messages

Email/Phone

Guest Name

_____

Wishes & Messages

_____

_____

_____

_____

_____

_____
Email/Phone

Guest Name

Wishes & Messages

EMAIL/PHONE

Guest Name

_____

Wishes & Messages

_____

_____

_____

_____

_____

_____
Email/Phone
_____

GIFT LOG

Name / Email / phone

Gift

_____

_____

_____

_____

_____

_____

_____

_____

_____

_____

_____

_____

GIFT LOG

Name / Email / phone	Gift

GIFT LOG

Name /Email /phone	Gift

GIFT LOG

Name /Email /phone	Gift

GIFT LOG

Name /Email /phone	Gift

GIFT LOG

Name / Email / phone	Gift

GIFT LOG

Name / Email / phone	Gift

NOTES & PHOTO

NOTES & PHOTO

NOTES & PHOTO

NOTES & PHOTO

NOTES & PHOTO

Printed in the USA
CPSIA information can be obtained
at www.ICGtesting.com
LVHW070853061123
762867LV00012B/65